The twins were in a play.

It was a play of Cinderella.

Mum and Dad came to see it. Gran came too.

Fred was the prince. He had to sing a song.

Flick was a goose. She had to hiss at the ugly sisters.

The ugly sisters were bossy. They made Cinderella do the dusting.

Cinderella had an old dress and
a duster.

But then she got a nice new dress.

She got some silver slippers too.

Cinderella went to the palace.

She danced with the prince.

But then she ran away. She dropped a silver slipper.

The prince picked it up.

Cinderella ran home. Her ugly sisters went home too.

Cinderella had her old dress on.

The prince had
to knock on
the door.

He had to try
the slipper on
Cinderella and
her sisters.

But Fred had lost the slipper!
"Have my boot!" said Miss Hill.

The ugly sisters tried on the boot.

It was too loose. But they said, “It’s too tight!”

Cinderella tried on the boot.
It was too loose. But she said, "It fits!"

Mum and Dad liked the play.

"It was better than the cinema!" said Gran.